OPERA

OPERA

for organ

Kevin
Mayhew

We hope you enjoy the music in this book.
Further copies of this and our many other books are available
from your local music shop or Christian bookshop.

In case of difficulty, please contact the publisher direct by writing to:

The Sales Department
KEVIN MAYHEW LTD
Rattlesden
Bury St Edmunds
Suffolk IP30 0SZ

Phone 01449 737978
Fax 01449 737834

Please ask for our complete catalogue of outstanding Church Music.

Front Cover: *Dance* by Joseph Paelinck (1781-1839)
Courtesy of Whitford and Hughes, London /
The Bridgeman Art Library, London. Reproduced by kind permission.

Cover designed by Jaquetta Sergeant.

First published in Great Britain in 1997 by Kevin Mayhew Ltd.

ISBN 0 86209 992 7
ISMN M 57004 054 4
Catalogue No: 1400124

0 1 2 3 4 5 6 7 8 9

Music Editor: Rosalind Welch
Music setting by Chris Hinkins

Printed and bound in Great Britain

Contents

NESSUN DORMA from 'TURANDOT'

Giacomo Puccini (1858–1924) arr. Colin Mawby

9

NON PIÙ ANDRAI from 'THE MARRIAGE OF FIGARO'

Wolfgang Amadeus Mozart (1756–1791) arr. Andrew Gant

AU FOND DU TEMPLE SAINT from 'THE PEARL FISHERS'

Georges Bizet (1838–1875) arr. June Nixon

VOI CHE SAPETE from 'THE MARRIAGE OF FIGARO'

Wolfgang Amadeus Mozart (1756–1791) arr. June Nixon

SLEEP SONG from 'HANSEL AND GRETEL'

Engelbert Humperdinck (1854–1921) arr. Andrew Gant

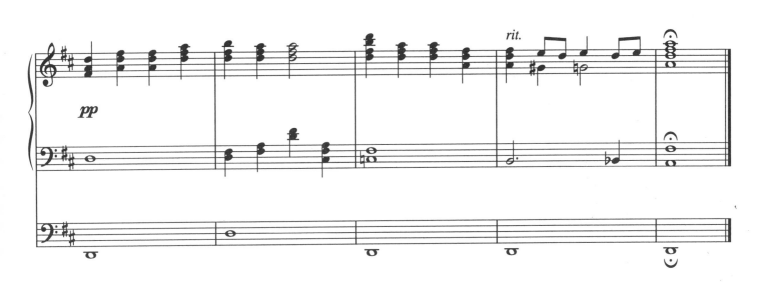

PAPAGENO'S ARIA from 'THE MAGIC FLUTE'

Wolfgang Amadeus Mozart (1756–1791) arr. Richard Lloyd

PILGRIMS' CHORUS from 'TANNHÄUSER'

Richard Wagner (1813–1883) arr. Colin Mawby

ONE FINE DAY from 'MADAME BUTTERFLY'

Giacomo Puccini (1858–1924) arr. Colin Mawby

29